PHONICS CHAPTER BOOK 11

TALES ONCE TOLD

AS RETOLD BY	ILLUSTRATED BY
Felix Pitre	**Rebecca Wildsmith**
Tai Lay	**Alexandra Wallner**
Yoko Mia Hirano	**Eileen Hine**
Jesús Cervantes	**Michael Grejniec**

Scholastic Inc.

New York   Toronto   London   Auckland   Sydney

Copyright © 1998 by Scholastic Inc.
Scholastic Phonics Chapter Books in design is a trademark of Scholastic Inc.
All rights reserved. Published by Scholastic Inc.
Printed in the U.S.A.
ISBN 0-590-03053-1

7 8 9 10   14   04 03 02 01 00

Dear Teacher/Family Member,

Scholastic Phonics Chapter Books provide early readers with interesting stories in easy-to-manage chapters. The books in this series are controlled for sounds and common sight words. Once sounds and sight words have been introduced, they are repeated frequently to give children lots of reading practice and to build children's confidence. When children experience success in reading, they want to read more, and when they read more, they become better readers.

Phonics instruction teaches children the way words work and gives them the strategies they need to become fluent, independent readers. However, phonics can only be effective when reading is meaningful and children have the opportunity to read many different kinds of books. Scholastic Phonics Chapter Books cover many curricular areas and genres. They are carefully designed to help build good readers, but more importantly, to inspire children to love reading.

Contents

Way back when, before there were books, people told stories to one another. The stories told about the world around them.

In this book, a storyteller sits with children around a campfire. The storyteller is telling stories about the sun and the moon, the water and the wind. Each of the stories is from a time long ago.

1 How Water Spoiled Sun's House

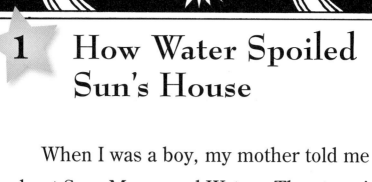

When I was a boy, my mother told me about Sun, Moon, and Water. The story is very old. It goes back to when Sun and Water both lived on the soil.

Sun and Water were good friends. Sun would often join Water at his home. Water always said in a happy voice, "I am glad you can join me, my friend."

Water's home was cold and moist. But after Sun had been there, it felt warmer.

One day, Sun said to his wife, Moon, "I feel sorry for Water, because he lives in such a cold, moist place."

"Why don't you have Water join us for dinner?" Moon asked. "When he feels how warm it is here, he'll see your point. He'll have no choice but to move."

So Sun told Water that he was having a party for him and his family.

"You have no choice, my friend," said Sun. "The point is, you've never been to my house. You must come."

"That is very kind of you, friend," said Water. "But your house is too small for us. We would spoil your house."

"With a little toil, I will make my house bigger," said Sun in a bold voice. "Then it can hold you and your family."

1   How Water Spoiled Sun's House

When I was a boy, my mother told me about Sun, Moon, and Water. The story is very old. It goes back to when Sun and Water both lived on the soil.

Sun and Water were good friends. Sun would often join Water at his home. Water always said in a happy voice, "I am glad you can join me, my friend."

Water's home was cold and moist. But after Sun had been there, it felt warmer.

One day, Sun said to his wife, Moon, "I feel sorry for Water, because he lives in such a cold, moist place."

"Why don't you have Water join us for dinner?" Moon asked. "When he feels how warm it is here, he'll see your point. He'll have no choice but to move."

So Sun told Water that he was having a party for him and his family.

"You have no choice, my friend," said Sun. "The point is, you've never been to my house. You must come."

"That is very kind of you, friend," said Water. "But your house is too small for us. We would spoil your house."

"With a little toil, I will make my house bigger," said Sun in a bold voice. "Then it can hold you and your family."

Sun ran home and started to work.

"My friend Water will not be cold," he sang in a loud voice. "He will move near me and feel as warm as gold."

Sun toiled all day, moving rocks and soil. When he was done, he smiled. "Tomorrow I will invite Water and his family to join us."

The next day Water and his family came to Sun's house.

"Come in, friend," called out Sun. "Join us in here where it is not cold."

So Water began to move his family into Sun's house. Fish and frogs and whales swam in with Water. They made a great noise. Soon there was water all the way up to Sun's knees.

"Is it still safe to come in, or have we spoiled your house?" asked Water.

"You haven't spoiled it," called out Sun. "There's always room for a friend."

In swam tadpoles and seals. The water was now up to Sun's nose!

"Is there still room?" called Water.

Moon tried to point out to Sun that their house was spoiled, but Sun couldn't hear her over the noise. Besides, Sun wanted to show that he was right. So he moved up to the roof with his wife. Then he yelled down in a loud voice, "Come on in. There's still lots of room."

Then Water flowed and flowed and flowed into Sun's house. Soon it reached the roof. Sun and Moon had no choice. They folded up their clothes and left the moist house. They moved to the sky. And that is where Sun and Moon live to this day.

2 The Voyage to the Sun

One day, Sun sent a spark of life to Earth. The spark made its voyage down the rays of Sun. It moved through the sky and came to a village. The spark landed in a young woman's house and turned into a small boy.

The children in the village all played together, but the boy avoided playing with them. He would not join in their games.

The boy didn't know where his father was, and this made him sad. He said to his mother, "I have made a choice. I must go look for my father, but I'll always be loyal to you."

The boy's mother wasn't happy, but she understood. So the boy gave his mother a hug and left home.

Soon the boy met the Corn Planter. "Can you lead me to my father?" the boy asked. The Corn Planter didn't answer. He just kept turning the soil to make his corn plants grow.

The boy went on his way and met the
Pot Maker. "Can you lead me to my father?"
he asked. The Pot Maker didn't say a word.
She just kept shaping moist clay into pots.

The boy didn't want to spoil her work, so
he moved on. He was angry because no one
had given him an answer, and he missed his
mother. The boy wanted to go home, but he
had to find his father.

The boy walked on and on and came to the Arrow Maker. Again, the boy asked for help finding his father. At first, he got no answer, but the Arrow Maker was wise and saw that the boy had come from the Sun.

The Arrow Maker said he would help. He made a long, smooth arrow and put the boy on it. Then he pointed the arrow toward the sky. He shot the arrow, and the boy rode to the Sun.

When the boy met the mighty Sun, he
was filled with joy. "I am your son!" he
called.

"Perhaps you are my son. Perhaps you
are not. If you pass four tests, I will know
the truth," Sun said.

"First, you must protect yourself against
the claws and teeth of the beasts in the cave.
Then, you must avoid the poison in the pit of
the snakes. After that, you must walk next
to the beehives without being stung. At last,
you must show that the noise made by
thunder does not frighten you."

The brave boy said, "Father, I will
pass the tests."

The boy was careful and clever. He took
care not to annoy the beasts as he walked
through the cave. He moved slowly in the
pit, so as not to disturb the swaying snakes.
He made sure not to brush against the
beehives and destroy the bee's honey. Then
when the thunder boomed, the boy put his
hands over his ears. He was not frightened,
and he passed the four tests.

The boy and his father joined hands
and were very happy. Sun was so proud
of the boy. The Sun gave the boy some of
his power. Then Sun said to him, "Now
you must go back to Earth."

Once again, the boy rode on the arrow.
This time, the arrow pointed toward Earth.
When the arrow reached Earth, the boy
ran back to his village. The people
of the village were joyful. The boy had
come home.

3 Moon's Knapsack

Once, Sun, Moon, and Wind were brothers and sisters. They lived under their mother's watchful eye. Their mother was a bright star who was well known for the beautiful things she could knit.

One night, Grandmother and Grandfather were having a big dinner party. Everyone knew they had a knack for making great food. Sun, Moon, and Wind couldn't wait to go!

When it was time for the party, Mother told her three children, "My knees are hurting me. I will stay home, but you go and have fun."

Mother went over to hug them, but Sun and Wind ducked out from under her hug. They raced away to see who could get to the party first. They knew there would be many tasty dishes for dinner, and they each wanted to be at the front of the line.

Moon did not rush off. She kneeled by her Mother and asked, "What will you do all night?"

Mother told Moon, "I will work on my knitting. I have to undo some knots in it. You go on to the party. I'll be fine."

When Sun got to the dinner party, he knocked on the front door. Then he turned the knob and let himself in. He rushed for the food, knocking things down along the way. He ate and ate until he could eat no more. Then Sun took a nap under a chair.

When Wind got to the party, he did not even stop to knock at the front door. He danced right by Grandmother without saying hello. He stood up on a chair and looked to see who he knew. Then he ate and ate until he could eat no more.

Soon, Moon got to the party. She knocked at the front door. Grandmother showed her in and asked where Mother was. Moon told her that Mother had stayed home to knit because her knees hurt.

The party was so much fun! Moon wished that Mother could see it. She knew Mother would love to taste the food. So Moon cut off a little bit of each kind of food with a small knife and put the food into her knapsack.

When the children got home, Mother
put down her knitting and asked, "How was
the party?"

Sun said, "It was great! I ate lots of
sweets!"

Wind said, "I saw friends I knew and ate
so much good food."

Then Moon kneeled in front of Mother.
She opened her knapsack and gave Mother
some food. "I know your knees hurt, and you
must be hungry," she said.

Mother was angry. She turned to Sun and said, "You knew my knees hurt, but you did not think of me. From now on you will be very hot. People will not want to stand under you."

To this day when the sun comes out, people hide in the shade.

Then Mother said to Wind, "You, too, thought only of your own fun. From now on you will blow strong gusts of air that can blow away houses. People will know how mean you can be."

And so to this day, people are not happy when the wind blows hard.

Then Mother kneeled down in front of Moon. She said, "Moon, I know you did not forget me. You thought of me knitting by myself at home. From now on, you will be cool and have a soft, bright light. People will always be happy standing under you."

And so to this day, people are glad to see the beautiful moon in the sky.

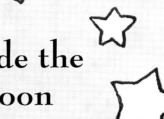

4 How Wren Made the Sun and the Moon

Once upon a time, there was no sun. There was no moon. There was no sunlight to shine on the world and there was no moonlight. The only light on the world came from the stars. Though the world had no sun, there were some plants and animals there.

"Something's wrong here," thought a wren. "The world must have a sun so more plants and animals can grow!"

The wren thought and thought. "I've got it!" she cried. "One of us will become the sun!"

Wren wrote a note to the animals. This is what she wrote.

Dear friends,
    I am writing
to invite you to
wrestle in a contest.
The best wrestler
will become the sun.
    See you there,
        Wren

It was time for the contest. Four wrestlers came. They brought other animals to cheer. Wren brought her friend the rabbit.

The four animals wrestled and wrestled to see who was the best wrestler. The wrestlers wriggled this way and they wriggled that way. Each one wanted to be the sun.

After a long time, the contest was over. Wrinkles, the dog, was the winner! Wrinkles was the best wrestler of all!

The wren cheered. The rabbit wriggled his ears and wrinkled his nose. They were happy that from now on Wrinkles would be the sun.

Tecoo, the monkey, though, was not happy. Tecoo thought he was the best wrestler, even though he had lost the wrestling contest.

Tecoo shouted, "The animals are wrong for not making me the sun! They are wrong, wrong, wrong! I want so very much to be the sun."

"I am ready to be the sun," said Wrinkles.

"Not yet," said Wren. "There is one more thing you must do. I will write a note, to tell you all about it."

When Wren had written the note, Wrinkles read it. This is what she wrote.

Dear Wrinkles,
    Don't tell this to anyone. You must walk into the light of the great North Star. Then you will become the sun!
                Wren

Now Tecoo had to think of a plan fast.

The great North Star twinkled at the top of the sky. It brought a ray of light to the world. Soon it was time for Wrinkles to walk into the starlight. But Tecoo pushed Wrinkles and stepped into the starlight with him!

The world lit up! Wrinkles was now the sun. Tecoo was now the moon. Each was as bright as the other.

"It is wrong that the moon is as bright as the sun," Wren said. "The point is that Wrinkles was the best wrestler. Tecoo should not have pushed him."

Then Rabbit said, "I know a way to make the sun shine brighter than the moon." With that, the rabbit jumped into the sky in front of the moon. Now the moon was not so bright. Though it was still bright, it was no longer as bright as the sun.

To this day, the sun is brighter than the moon. Sometimes, on a clear night, you can still see the shadow of the brave little rabbit who jumped into the moon.

The children looked up, hoping to the see the rabbit's shadow. The storyteller just smiled.

31

PHONICS

Decodable Words With the Phonic Elements

1 oi

choice	point
join	soil
moist	spoil
noise	toil
	voice

2 oy

oy	oi
annoy	avoid
boy	choice
destroy	join
joy	moist
joyful	noise
voyage	pointed
	poison
	soil
	spoil

3 kn

knack	knob
knapsack	knock
kneeled	knots
knees	know
knife	known
knit	

4 wr

wren	write
wriggled	written
Wrinkles	wrong
wrinkled	wrote